101 Jazz & B▬▬▬ for Bus▬

Piano/Organ Edition with Guitar Chords.

28'
34
35?
40
44 Dave
54
64 dave
(64)
68?
92?
97

Wise Publications
London/New York/Sydney/Cologne

Exclusive Distributors:
Music Sales Limited
8/9 Frith Street, London W1V 5TZ, England
Music Sales Pty. Limited
120 Rothschild Avenue, Rosebery, NSW 2018, Australia

This book © Copyright 1985 by
Wise Publications
ISBN 0.7119.0727.7
Order No. AM 60245

Art direction by Mike Bell.
Cover illustration by Alistair Graham.
Compiled and arranged by Peter Lavender.
Processed by Hillmob Music Services.

Music Sales complete catalogue lists thousands of
titles and is free from your local music book shop,
or direct from Music Sales Limited.
Please send £1.00 in stamps for postage to
Music Sales Limited, 8/9 Frith Street, London W1V 5TZ.

Printed and bound in Great Britain by
Anchor Press Ltd, Tiptree, Essex

1
African Waltz

Words & Music by Galt MacDermot

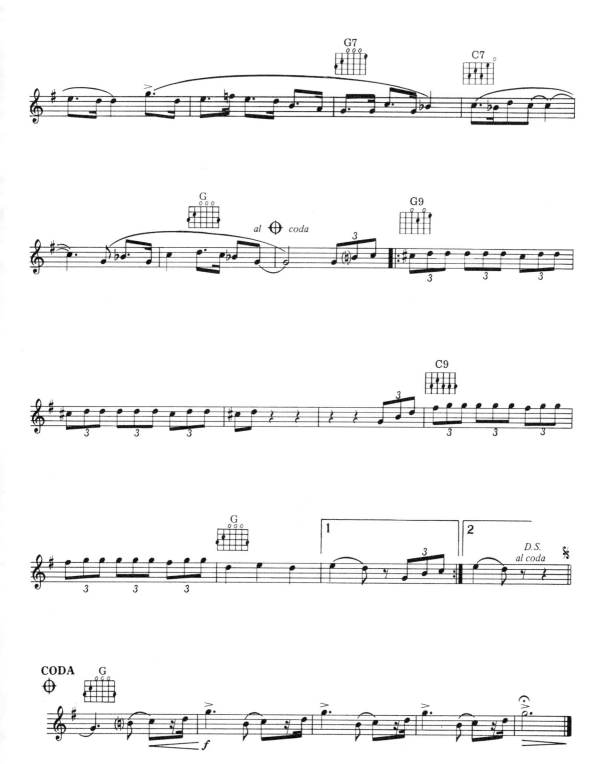

2
Air Conditioned Jungle

Words & Music by Duke Ellington

3
Angel Eyes

Words by Earl Brent
Music by Matt Dennis

Try to think___ that love's not a-round,___ still it's un-com-fort-'bly near.

___ My old heart___ ain't gain-in' no ground___ be-cause my an-gel eyes ain't here.

___ An-gel eyes___ that old dev-il sent, ___ they glow un-bear-a-bly bright.

___ Need I say___ that my love's mis-spent,___ mis-spent with an-gel eyes to-night.

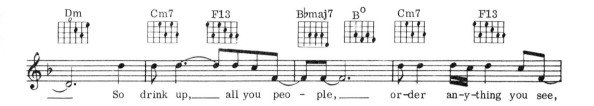

So drink up,___ all you peo - ple, ___ or-der an-y-thing you see,

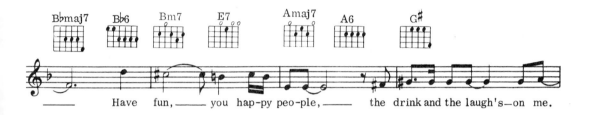

Have fun, ___ you hap-py peo-ple, ___ the drink and the laugh's—on me.

Par-don me, — but I "got-ta run", ___ the fact's un-com-mon-ly clear,

Got-ta find___who's now num-ber one ___ and why my an-gel eyes ain't here.

'Scuse me while I dis - ap - pear.___

4
Baby Won't You Please Come Home

Words & Music by
Charles Warfield & Clarence Williams

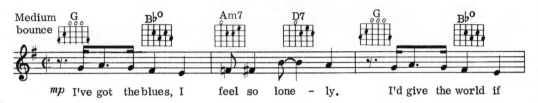

mp I've got the blues, I feel so lone - ly. I'd give the world if

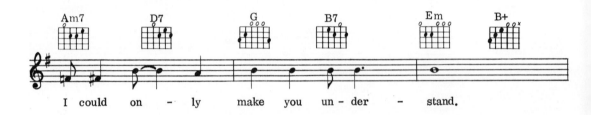

I could on - ly make you un - der - stand.

It sure - ly would be grand. I'm goin' to tel - e - graph you ba - by,

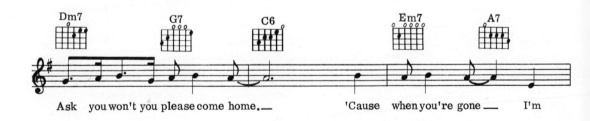

Ask you won't you please come home. __ 'Cause when you're gone __ I'm

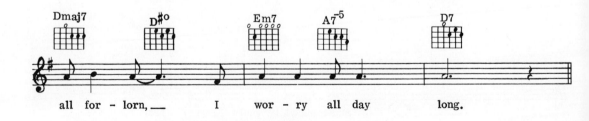

all for - lorn, __ I wor - ry all day long.

5
Basin Street Blues

Words & Music by Spencer Williams

6
Big Noise From Winnetka

Words by Gil Rodin & Bob Crosby
Music by Bob Haggart & Ray Baudac

1. Big Noise blew in from Win-net-ka Stole each girl-ie's heart and then Big Noise blew in from Win-net- - ka Big Noise blew right out a-gain Girls were sigh-ing, their boy-friends cry-ing, their hearts were break-ing when Big Noise blew in from Win-net - ka Stop, Look, List - en, lis-ten to the Big Noise

2. I'm called Big Noise from Win-net-ka And I play ro-man-tic parts. I just blew in from Win-net- - ka Where I broke a mil-lion hearts. Now I've had my fun and yet, there's just one who got me from the start Ex - it Big Noise from Win-net - ka Big Noise blew right out a-gain. En-ter Big Noise in your heart.

7
Bill Bailey Won't You Please Come Home

Traditional

"Won't you come home, Bill Bail-ey? Won't you come home?" She moans the whole day long. ___ "I'll do the cook-ing, dar-ling, I'll pay the rent, I know I've done you wrong. ___ 'Mem-ber that rain-y eve that I drove you out with noth-ing but a fine tooth comb? ___ I know I'm to blame, Well ain't that a shame? Bill Bail-ey won't you please come home?" ___ home?" ___

8
Black Coffee

Words & Music by
Paul Francis Webster & Sonny Burke

(Girl) I'm feel-in' might-y lone-some, Have-n't slept a wink. I
(Boy) I'm feel-in' might-y lone-some, Have-n't slept a wink. I

walk the floor and watch the door and in bet-ween I drink Black Cof-fee, _____
walk the floor and watch the door and in bet-ween I drink Black Cof-fee, _____

Love's a hand-me-down broom. _____ I'll nev-er know a Sun-day,
Since my gal went a-way. _____ My nerves have gone to piec-es,

In this week-day room. _____ I'm talk-in' to the shad-ows,
And my hair's turn-in gray. _____ I'm talk-in' to the shad-ows,

One o'clock to four. And Lord how slow the mo-ments go when all I do is pour Black
One o'clock to four. And Lord how slow the mo-ments go when all I do is pour Black

Cof-fee, _____ Since the blues caught my eye. _____ I'm
Cof-fee, _____ Love's a sor-ry af-fair. I

hang-in' out on Mon-day my Sun-day dreams to dry. _____
know where all the blues are, 'Cause, ba-by I've been there. _____

9
Boogie Woogie Bugle Boy

Words & Music by
Don Raye & Hughie Prince

Medium Boogie Woogie

He was a fa-mous trum-pet man from out Chi - ca- go way,__ He had a "boo-gie" style that no-one

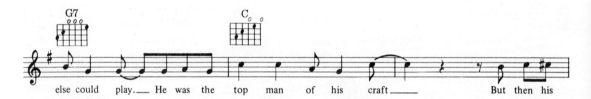

else could play.__ He was the top man of his craft__ But then his

num-ber came up,__ And he was gone with the draft. He's in the ar-my now a-blow-in' re-veil-le, He's the

Boo-gie Woo-gie Bu - gle Boy of Com-pa-ny B.__ They 1. made him blow a bu-gle for his
2. puts the boys to sleep with "boogie"

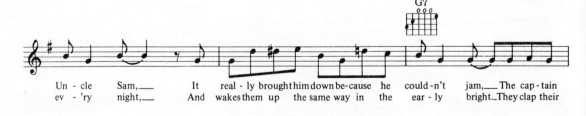

Un - cle   Sam,__   It   real - ly brought him down be-cause he   could-n't   jam,__ The cap - tain
ev - 'ry   night,__   And   wakes them up   the same way in   the   ear - ly   bright. They clap their

10
Bugle Call Rag

Words & Music by
Jack Pettis, Billy Meyers & Elmer Schoebel

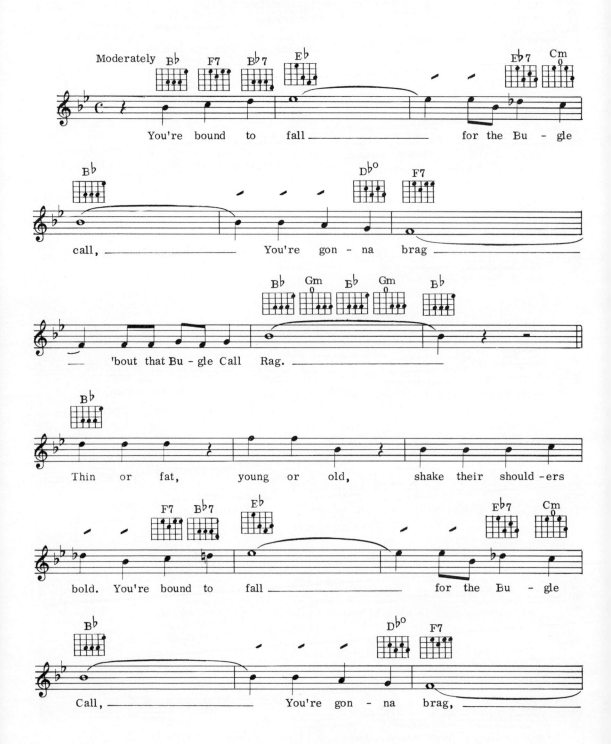

11
Chelsea Bridge

By Billy Strayhorn

lights of London Town be-gan ___ to flick - er down, My dreams began to drown one by

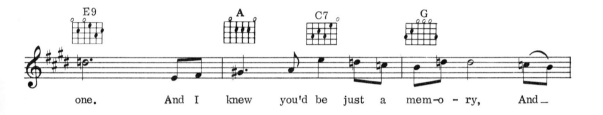

one. And I knew you'd be just a mem-o - ry, And ___

our love was o - ver and done, Oooh, _____ Blue was I ___

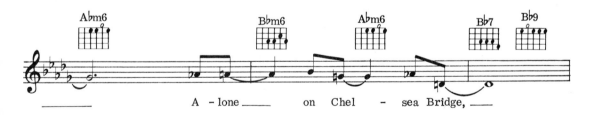

_____ A - lone ___ on Chel - sea Bridge, ___

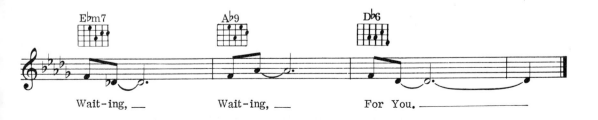

Wait-ing, ___ Wait-ing, ___ For You. _____

12
Cinnamon And Clove

Music by Johnny Mandel
Words by Marilyn Bergman & Alan Bergman

13
The Creole Love Call

Words & Music by Duke Ellington

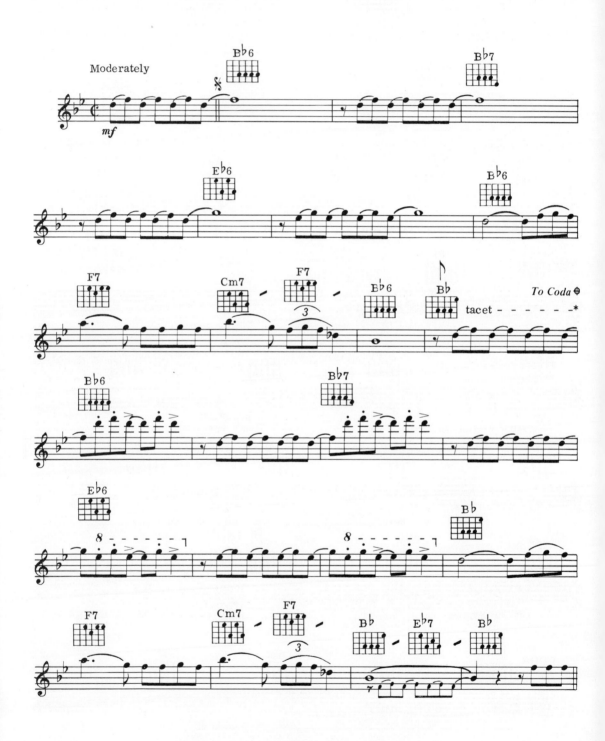

14
Canal Street Blues

By Joe 'King' Oliver

15
Cute

Words by Stanley Styne
Music by Neal Hefti

16
Don't Dream Of Anybody But Me
(Li'l Darlin')

Words by Bart Howard
Music by Neal Hefti

Intro |F9 |Fm7|F9|Fm7|

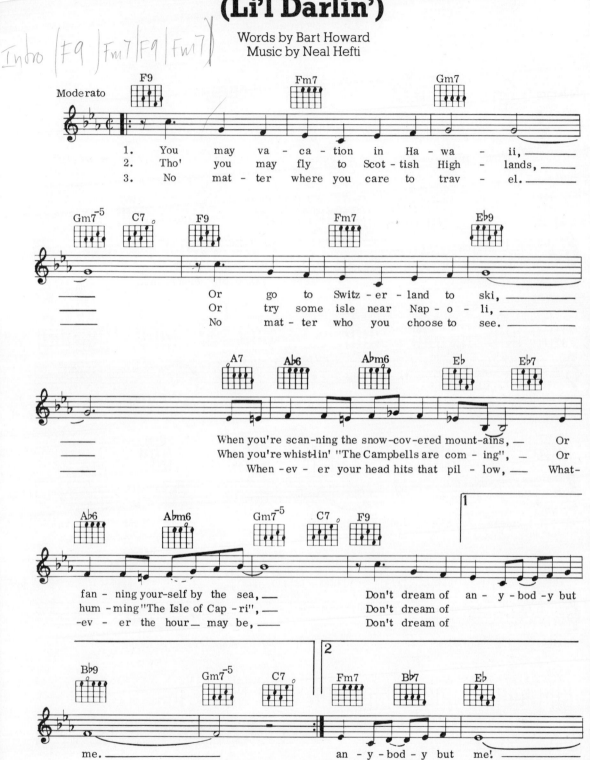

1. You may va-ca-tion in Ha-wa-ii, ___
2. Tho' you may fly to Scot-tish High-lands, ___
3. No mat-ter where you care to trav-el. ___

___ Or go to Switz-er-land to ski, ___
___ Or try some isle near Nap-o-li, ___
___ No mat-ter who you choose to see.

When you're scan-ning the snow-cov-ered mount-ains, — Or
When you're whist-lin' "The Campbells are com-ing", — Or
When-ev-er your head hits that pil-low, — What-

fan-ning your-self by the sea, ___ Don't dream of an-y-bod-y but
hum-ming "The Isle of Cap-ri", ___ Don't dream of
-ev-er the hour_ may be, ___ Don't dream of

me. ___ an-y-bod-y but me!

17
Don't Get Around Much Anymore

Words by Bob Russell
Music by Duke Ellington

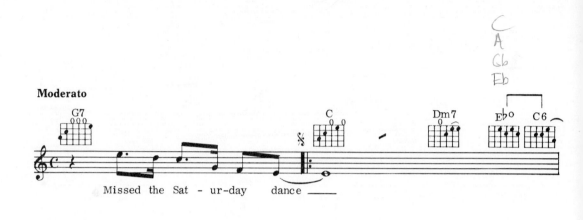

Missed the Sat - ur-day dance ____

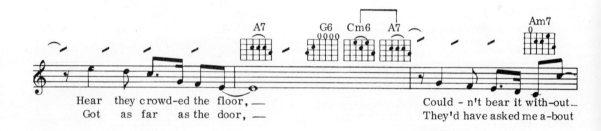

Hear they crowd-ed the floor, ____   Could - n't bear it with-out ___
Got as far as the door, ____   They'd have asked me a-bout

____ you, ____   Don't get a-round much an - y - more.
____ you, ____   Don't get a-round much an - y -

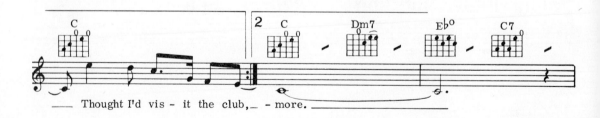

____ Thought I'd vis - it the club, __ - more. ____

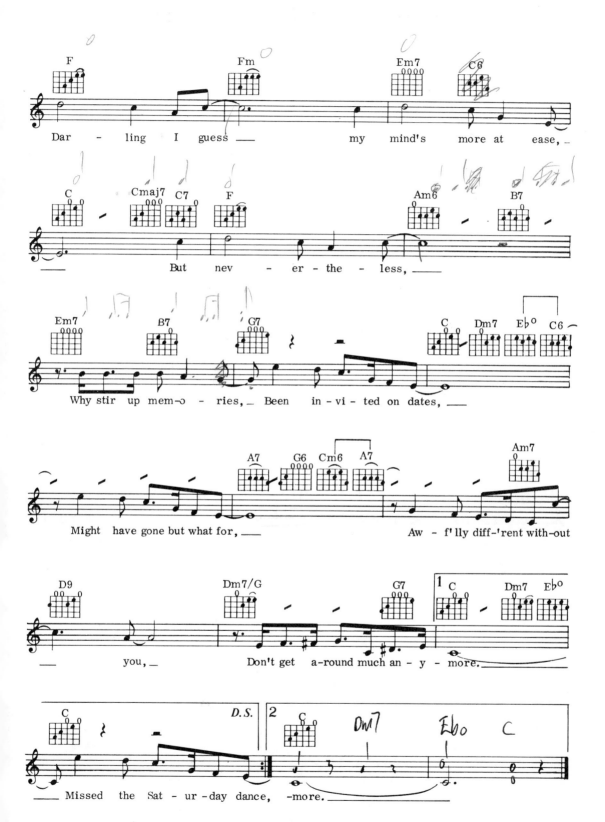

18
Drop Me Off In Harlem

Words by Nick Kenny
Music by Duke Ellington

19
East Of The Sun
(And West Of The Moon)

Words & Music by Brooks Bowman

20
Emanon

By Dizzy Gillespie & Milt Shaw

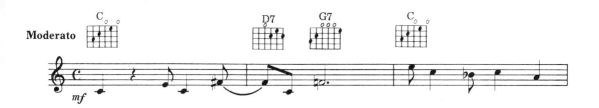

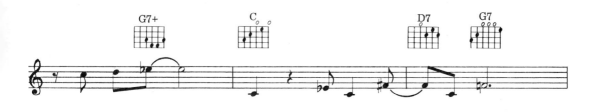

D.C. & ad lib solos

21
The Entertainer

By Scott Joplin

22
Farewell Blues

Words & Music by Elmer Schoebel, Paul Mares & Leon Rappolo

23
For Dancers Only

Music by Sy Oliver
Words by Don Raye & Vic Schoen

Danc - ers, please lis - ten to me___ while I sing___
___ you a song___ you should hear.___ Danc - ers, this
song was es - pe - cial-ly writ - ten for you.___ So lend an ear.___ Oh, it's
not for peo - ple who sing sweet, Or for oth - er folks who
can't stand heat.___ And it's not for floo-gies with two left feet!
It's For Danc-ers On-ly.___ Oh, it's not for old folks who aren't hep.

24
For Lena And Lenny

By Quincy Jones

25
Flying Home

By Benny Goodman & Lionel Hampton

26
Four

By Miles Davis

27
Frustration

By Duke Ellington

28
Georgia On My Mind

Words by Stuart Gorrell
Music by Hoagy Carmichael

Mel - o - dies   bring   mem - o - ries   that
By - gone days   of   hap - pi - ness   still

ling - er   in   my   heart, ___   Make me think   of   Geor - gia.   Why
haunt me   all   the   while, ___   Noth - ing could   com - pare with   my

did we ___   ev - er   part? ___   Some sweet   day   when
Geor - gia's ___   sun - ny   smile; ___   That is   why   I

blos - soms fall,   and   all   the   world's a   song, ___
of - ten   sigh   as   down   the   trail   I   roam, ___

I'll go   back   to   Geor - gia,   'cause   that's where ___ I   be - long.
Long - ing for   sweet   Geor - gia   be - cause it ___ is   my   home.

29
Go Away Blues

Words & Music by Duke Ellington

30
Green Onions

Music by Booker T. Jones, Steve Cropper,
Al Jackson Jr. & Lewie Steinberg

D.S. and Fade

31
Hey! Ba-Ba-Re-Bop

Words & Music by
Lionel Hampton & Curley Hammer

32
The Hawk Talks

By Louis Bellson

33
Honeysuckle Rose

Music by Thomas 'Fats' Waller
Words by Andy Razaf

34
House Of The Rising Sun

Traditional

35
I'll Remember April

Words & Music by Don Raye, Gene de Paul & Patricia Johnson

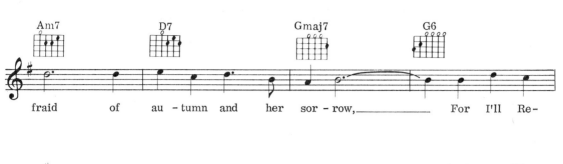

fraid   of   au -tumn and   her   sor - row,_____   For   I'll   Re-

mem -ber_____   A - pril   and   you._____

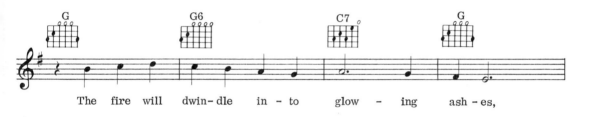

The   fire   will   dwin-dle   in - to   glow   -   ing   ash - es,

For flames and   love   live such a   lit - tle while. _____   I

won't   for-get, _____   but   I won't   be   lone - ly,_____   I'll   Re-

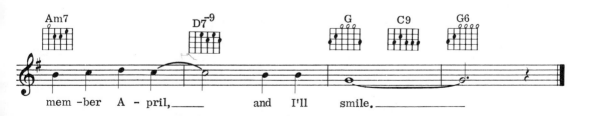

mem -ber   A - pril,_____   and   I'll   smile._____

36
I Ain't Got Nobody
(And There's Nobody Cares For Me)

Words & Music by
Roger Graham & Spencer Williams

37
I'm Beginning To See The Light

Words & Music by
Harry James, Duke Ellington, Johnny Hodges & Don George

38
In A Sentimental Mood

Words & Music by
Duke Ellington, Irving Mills & Manny Kurtz

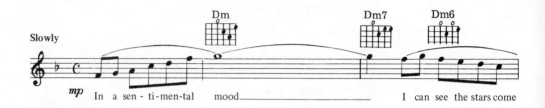

Slowly

In a sen-ti-men-tal mood _____ I can see the stars come

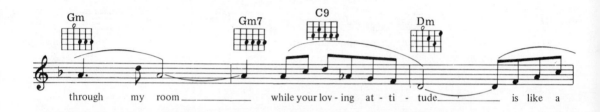

through my room _____ while your lov-ing at-ti-tude _____ is like a

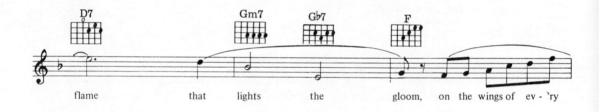

flame that lights the gloom, on the wings of ev-'ry

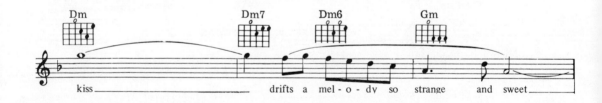

kiss drifts a mel-o-dy so strange and sweet _____

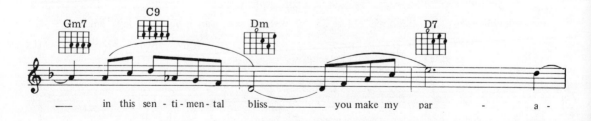

_____ in this sen-ti-men-tal bliss _____ you make my par - a -

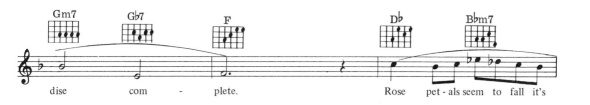

dise com - plete. Rose pet - als seem to fall it's

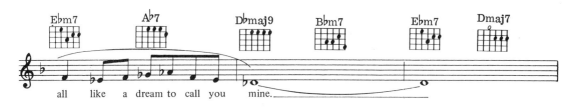

all like a dream to call you mine.

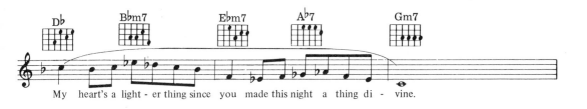

My heart's a light - er thing since you made this night a thing di - vine.

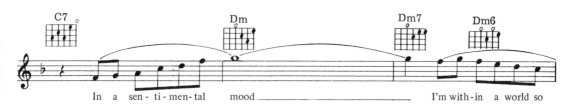

In a sen - ti - men - tal mood I'm with - in a world so

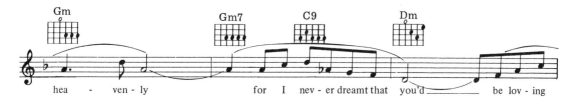

hea - ven - ly for I nev - er dreamt that you'd be lov - ing

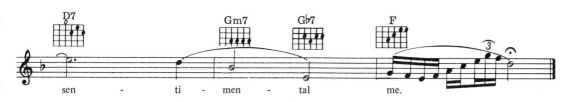

sen - ti - men - tal me.

39
Is You Is, Or Is You Ain't
(Ma' Baby)

Words & Music by
Billy Austin & Louis Jordan

40
It Don't Mean A Thing
(If It Ain't Got That Swing)

Words by Irving Mills
Music by Duke Ellington

It don't mean a thing, if it ain't got that swing,

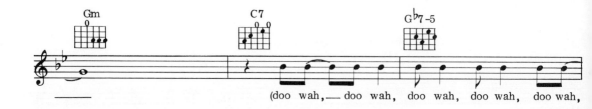

(doo wah,— doo wah, doo wah, doo wah, doo wah,

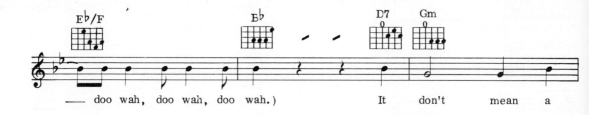

— doo wah, doo wah, doo wah.) It don't mean a

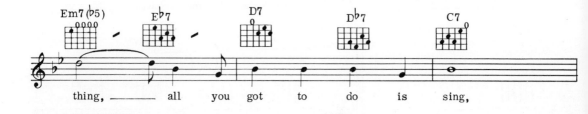

thing, ——— all you got to do is sing,

(doo wah,— doo wah, doo wah, doo wah, doo wah,— doo wah, doo wah, doo

41
It's A Raggy Waltz

Music by Dave Brubeck

42
The Joint Is Jumpin'

Words by Andy Razaf & J C Johnson
Music by Thomas Waller

They have a new ex-pres-sion, A-long old Har-lem way, That tells you when a par-ty is ten times more than gay; To say that things are jump-in', Leaves not a sin-gle doubt, That ev-'ry-thing is in full swing,_ When you hear some-one shout:

The Joint Is Jump-in', It's real-ly jump-in'
The Joint Is Jump-in', It's real-ly jump-in'

Come in cats,_ and check your hats,_ I mean this joint is jump-in'.
Ev-'ry Mose_ is on his toes,_ I mean this joint is jump-in'.

43
John Hardy's Wife

By Mercer Ellington

44
The Lonesome Road

Words by Gene Austin
Music by Nathaniel Shilkret

mf Look down, look down, that lone - some road, Be -
fore you trav - el on. Look up, look up, and
see yo' Mak - er, 'fore Gabri - el blows his horn.
Wear - y to - tin' such a load, Tredg - ing down that
lone - some road. Look down, look down, that lone - some
road, Be - fore you trav - el on. Look

45
Lean Baby

Words by Roy Alfred
Music by Billy May

Medium bounce

mf My Lean Ba - by, tall___ and thin.__ Five feet sev - en of

bones and skin,__ but when she tells me may-be she___ loves me__ I feel as

mel-low as a fel-low can be.___ She's so skin- ny, She's__

____ so drawn,__ When she stands side-ways you think she's gone,_ But when she

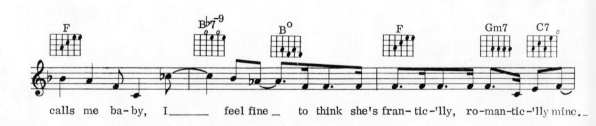

calls me ba-by, I___ feel fine _ to think she's fran-tic-'lly, ro-man-tic-'lly mine._

46
Lonesome
(Si Tu Vois Ma Mère)

By Sydney Bechet

47
Lover Man
(Oh Where Can You Be)

Words & Music by
Jimmy Davis, Roger Ram Ramirez & Jimmy Sherman

Moderately slow

mf I don't know why, but I'm feel-ing so sad. —

I long to try some-thing I've nev-er had. — Nev-er had no kiss-in',

Oh, what I've been miss-in', Lov-er Man, oh where can you be?

The night is cold, and I'm so all a-lone. — I'd give my soul just to

call you my own. — Got a moon a-bove me, But no one to love me,

48
Lullaby Of Birdland

Music by George Shearing
Words by George David Weiss

Lul - la - by of bird-land that's what I_____ al - ways hear_____

when you sigh. Nev - er in my word-land could there be ways_to re-veal, _____ in a phrase

_____ how I feel! _____ Have you ev - er heard two tur - tle doves_ bill and coo _____

when they love? _____ That's the kind of mag - ic mu - sic we make _____ with our lips

when we kiss!____ And there's a weep - y old wil - low; _____

He real - ly knows how to cry! __ That's how I'd cry in my pil - low, ___

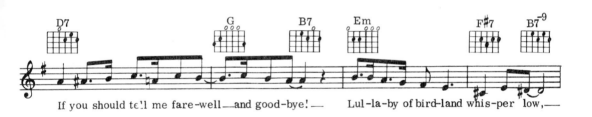
If you should tell me fare-well__and good-bye! __ Lul-la-by of bird-land whis-per low,___

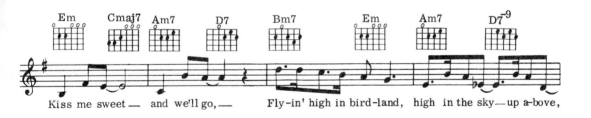
Kiss me sweet __ and we'll go, __ Fly-in' high in bird-land, high in the sky__up a-bove,

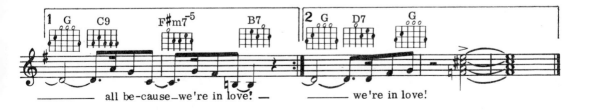
_____ all be-cause__we're in love! __ _____ we're in love!

49
Mama Don't Allow It

Words & Music by
Chas 'Cow Cow' Davenport

You've heard of the wo-man who lived in a shoe, What a dif-fi-cult time_ she had. For all of the kids seemed so an-xious to do all the things that would make her mad. A vis-i-tor called on them one day, And here's what he heard all the lit-tle kids say.

Ma-ma Don't Al-low no mu-sic played in here.____
Ma-ma Don't Al-low no pian-o play'n in here.____

Ma-ma Don't Al-low no mu-sic played in
Ma-ma Don't Al-low no pian-o play'n in

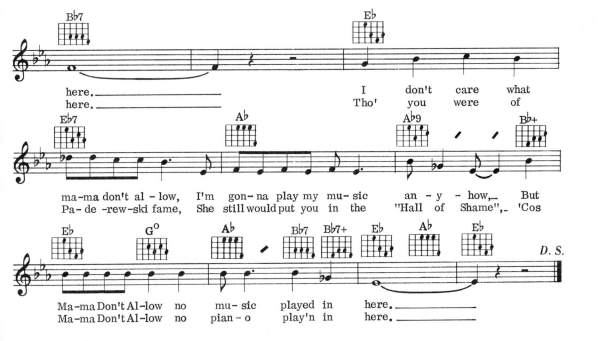

here._____
here._____

I don't care what
Tho' you were of

ma-ma don't al - low, I'm gon-na play my mu - sic an - y - how,___ But
Pa- de -rew-ski fame, She still would put you in the "Hall of Shame",_ 'Cos

Ma-ma Don't Al-low no mu- sic played in here._____
Ma-ma Don't Al-low no pian -- o play'n in here._____

D. S.

Mama Don't Allow no slap bass players in here,
Mama Don't Allow no slap bass players in here,
My mam claims it really is a sin,
To play upon a swollen violin,
So Mama Don't Allow no slap bass players in here.

Mama Don't Allow no truckin' done in here,
Mama Don't Allow no truckin' done in here,
After mama switches out the light,
I like to do my truckin' ev'ry night,
But Mama Don't Allow no truckin' done in here.

Mama Don't Allow no guitar players in here,
Mama Don't Allow no guitar players in here,
Makes no difference if you're flat or sharp,
You're gonna wake up playin' on a harp,
'Cos Mama Don't Allow no guitar players in here.

Mama Don't Allow no drummer man in here,
Mama Don't Allow no drummer man in here,
Mama says you're gonna go 'boom',
If she catch you drummin' in this room.
'Cos Mama Don't Allow no drummer man in here.

Mama Don't Allow no saxophones in here,
Mama Don't Allow no saxophones in here,
Ev'ry time she listens to a sax,
She feels so good she pays her income tax,
So Mama Don't Allow no saxophones in here.

Mama Don't Allow no Presley singin' here,
Mama Don't Allow no Presley singin' here,
I don't care what mama don't allow,
I'm gonna sing like Presley anyhow,
But Mama Don't Allow no Presley singers here.

Mama Don't Allow no nothin' done in here,
Mama Don't Allow no nothin' done in here,
Don't know how I'll ever get along,
'Cos when I'm doin' nothin', something's wrong!
But Mama Don't Allow no nothin' done in here.

50
Manteca

Words & Music by
Dizzy Gillespie & Gil Fuller

51
Memphis Blues

Words & Music by W.C. Handy

52
Midnight Sun

Words by Johnny Mercer
Music by Sonny Burke & Lionel Hampton

53
The Midnight Sun Will Never Set

Words by Dorcas Cochran
Music by Quincy Jones & Henri Salvador

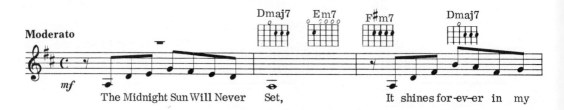

The Midnight Sun Will Never Set, It shines for-ev-er in my

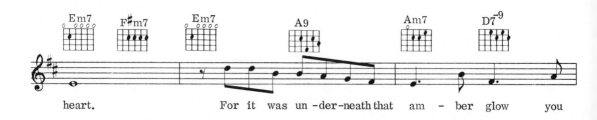

heart. For it was un -der-neath that am - ber glow you

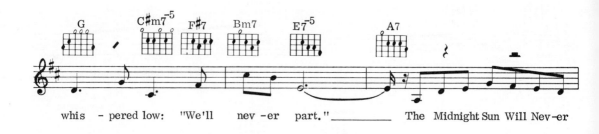

whis - pered low: "We'll nev -er part."_____ The Midnight Sun Will Nev -er

Set, So now could our ro-mance be through?

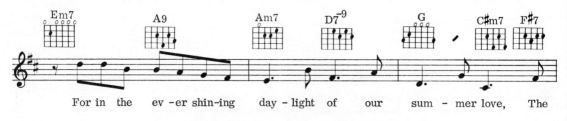

For in the ev -er shin-ing day - light of our sum - mer love, The

54
Mississippi Mud

Words & Music by Harry Barris

55
Mister Five By Five

Words & Music by Don Raye & Gene de Paul

56
Moanin'

Words by Jon Hendricks
Music by Bobby Timmons

Fairly slow

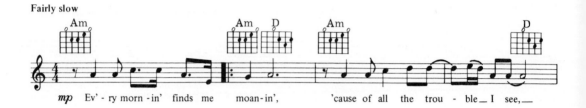

mp Ev'- ry morn -in' finds me moan-in', 'cause of all the trou - ble _ I see, _

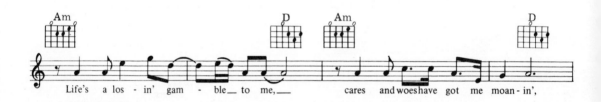

Life's a los - in' gam - ble _ to me, _ cares and woes have got me moan-in',

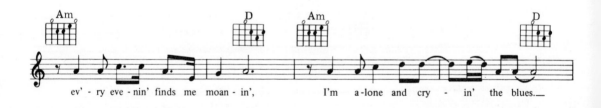

ev' - ry eve -nin' finds me moan-in', I'm a-lone and cry - in' the blues. _

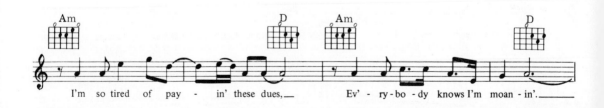

I'm so tired of pay - in' these dues, _ Ev' - ry-bo -dy knows I'm moan-in'. _____

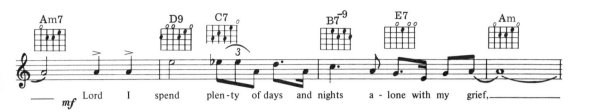

_mf_ Lord I spend plen-ty of days and nights a - lone with my grief,_____

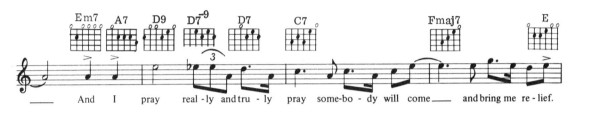

_____ And I pray real-ly and tru-ly pray some-bo-dy will come_____ and bring me re - lief.

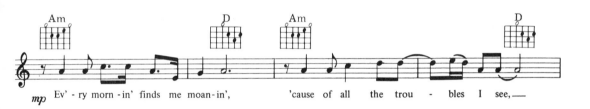

_mp_ Ev' - ry morn-in' finds me moan-in', 'cause of all the trou - bles I see, _____

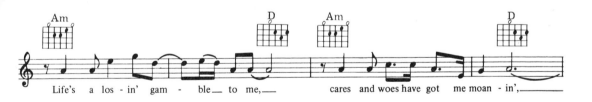

Life's a los-in' gam - ble_____ to me, _____ cares and woes have got me moan - in', _____

_____ Ev' - ry morn - in' finds me

57
The Mood I'm In

Words & Music by
Pete King & Paul Francis Webster

Brightly

1. I like to feel fan - cy free, I like to live young,
2. I like to hear op - 'ra or I like to read Joyce,

I like the old mer - ry - go - round. I like to play
I'm not the pre - dict - a - ble kind. What-ev - er the

lov - er, But don't like to get stung, I like my two feet on the
op - tion is, what-ev - er the choice, I like to make up my own

ground. I may date a girl light - ly and kiss her po -
mind. If the choice were to break up or kiss her and

-lite - ly, But will she get un - der my skin.
make up, I'll try not to lead with my chin.

Well, my friends, it all de - pends on the mood I'm

1.
in.

2.
I may

58
Mood Indigo

Words & Music by
Duke Ellington, Irving Mills and Albany Bigard.

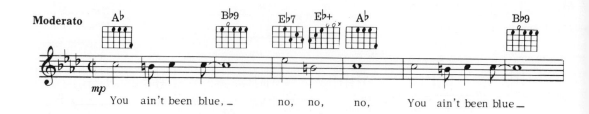

You ain't been blue, _ no, no, no, You ain't been blue _

Till you've had _ that mood in -di-go. That feel-in' goes _ steal-in'

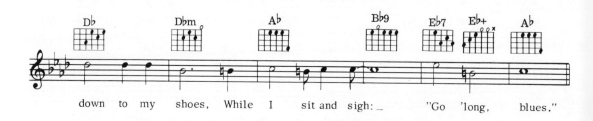

down to my shoes, While I sit and sigh: _ "Go 'long, blues."

Al-ways get that mood in-di-go _ Since my ba-by said good - bye.

In the eve - nin' when lights are low, _ I'm so lone-some I could

cry, 'Cause there's no - bo - dy who cares a - bout me, __

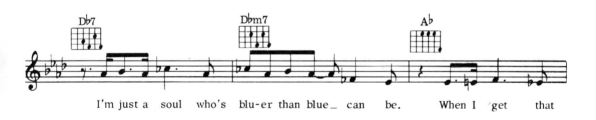

I'm just a soul who's blu-er than blue _ can be. When I 'get that

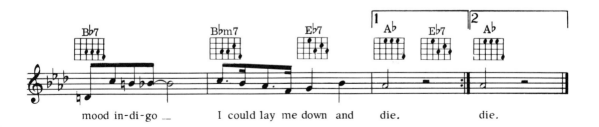

mood in-di-go __ I could lay me down and die. die.

59
A Night In Tunisia

Music by Frank Paparelli & John Dizzie Gillespie
Words by Raymond Leveen

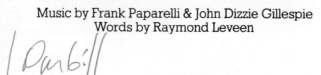

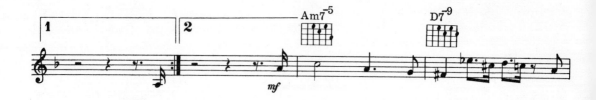

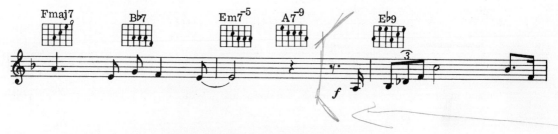

Repeat

60
Night Train

Words by Oscar Washington & Lewis C. Simpkins
Music by Jimmy Forrest

61
The Night We Called It A Day

Words by Tom Adair
Music by Matt Dennis

62
Oh Look At Me Now

Words by John DeVries
Music by Joe Bushkin

63
Ol' Man Mose

By Louis Armstrong & Zilner Trenton Randolph

One time there lived an ol' man with a ver-y crook-ed nose.__ He
I went 'round to the win-dow, and I peek'd in-to a crack.__ In-

lived in-side a log hut, and they called him 'Ol Man Mose.__ One
side there was an old man ly-ing flat up-on his back.__ I

dark and drear-y morn-ing I knocked up-on his door.__ I
thought that he was sleep-ing, His hand hung on the floor.__ He

did-n't hear a sin-gle sound, so I ain't gon-na do it no more; 'Cause_
did-n't make a sin-gle sound, so I ain't gon-na do it no more; 'Cause_

I be-lieve_ ol' man,_ I be-lieve_ ol' man,_
I found out _ ol' man,_ I found out_ ol' man,_

64
Midnight In Moscow

Based on a song by Vassili Soloviev & M. Matusovosky
New musical arrangement by Kenny Ball

65
Passion Flower

By Billy Strayhorn

66
The Peanut Vendor

Words by Marion Sunshine & L. Wolfe Gilbert
Music by Moises Simons

67
Perdido

Music by Juan Tizol
Words by Harry Lenk & Ervin Drake

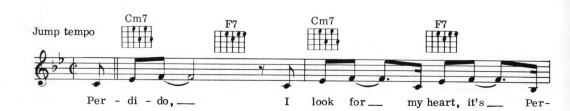

Per - di - do, ___ I look for ___ my heart, it's ___ Per-

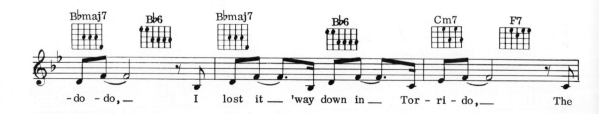

-do - do, ___ I lost it ___ 'way down in ___ Tor - ri - do, ___ The

day the fi - es - ta start - ed. ___ Bo-

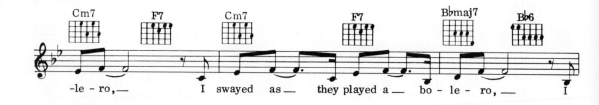

-le - ro, ___ I swayed as ___ they played a ___ bo - le - ro, ___ I

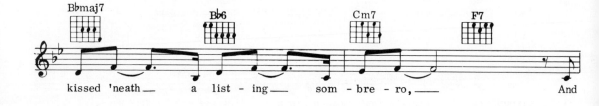

kissed 'neath ___ a list - ing ___ som - bre - ro, ___ And

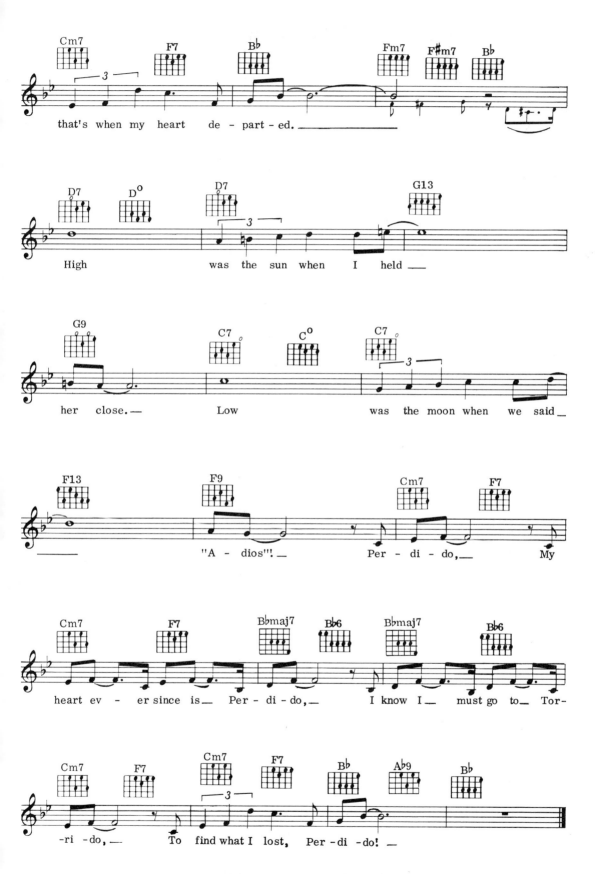

68
Petite Fleur
(Little Flower)

Words & Music by Sydney Bechet

69
The Preacher

By Horace Silver

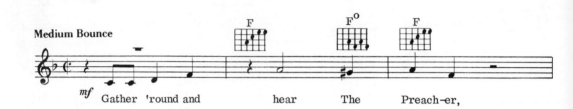

mf Gather 'round and   hear   The   Preach-er,

Hear   The   Preach-er,   Hear   The

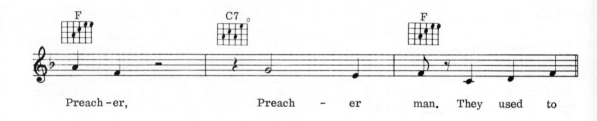

Preach-er,   Preach - er man. They used to

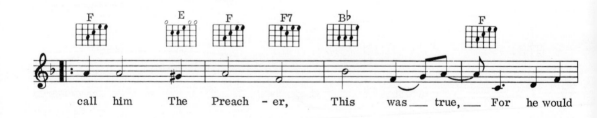

call him The Preach - er, This was___ true,___ For he would

preach from   his   heart   'bout the   on - ly   way he knew.___

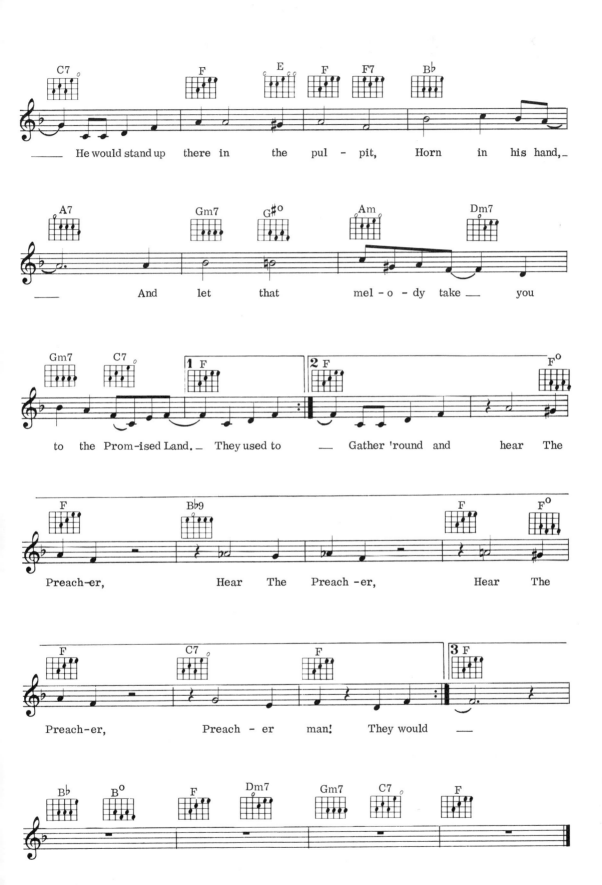

70
Primping At The Prom

By Duke Ellington

71
Raincheck

By Billy Strayhorn

72
Seven Eleven

By Carpenter & Williams

73
Satin Doll

Words by Johnny Mercer
Music by Duke Ellington & Billy Strayhorn

74
Short Stop

By Shorty Rogers

75
Skin Deep

By Louis Bellson

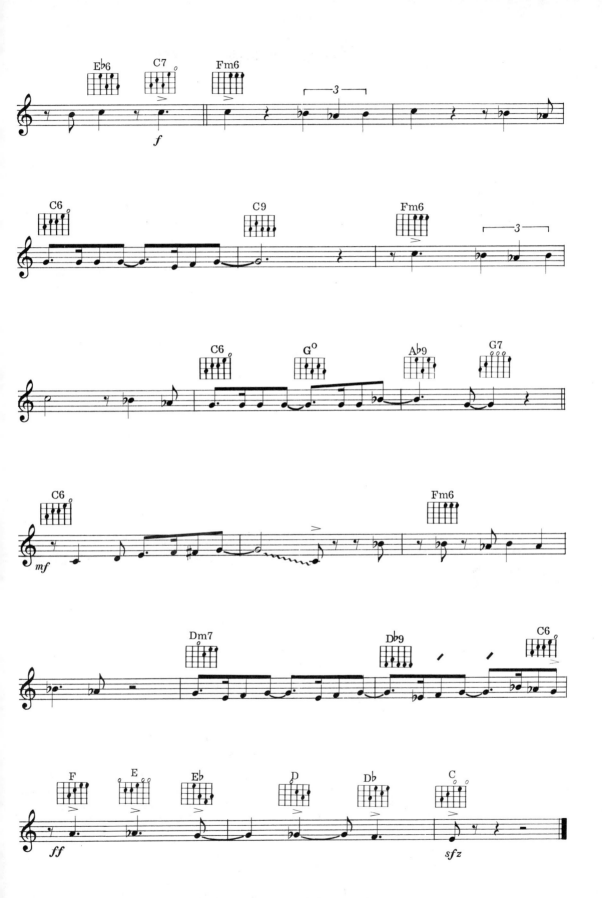

76
Slightly Out Of Tune
(Desafinado)

English lyrics by Jon Hendricks & Jessie Cavanaugh
Music by Antonio Carlos Jobim

77
Sophisticated Lady

Words by Irving Mills & Mitchell Parish
Music by Duke Ellington

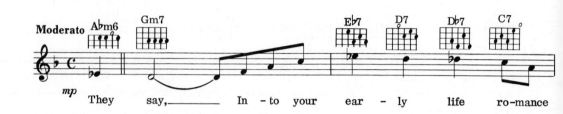

They say,_____ In - to your ear - ly life ro-mance

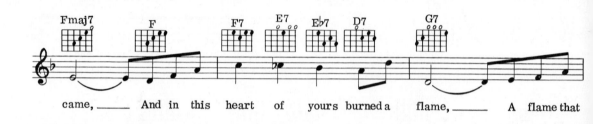

came,_____ And in this heart of yours burned a flame,_____ A flame that

flickered one day, And died a - way.

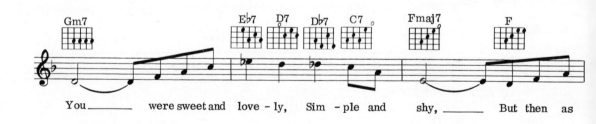

You_____ were sweet and love - ly, Sim - ple and shy,_____ But then as

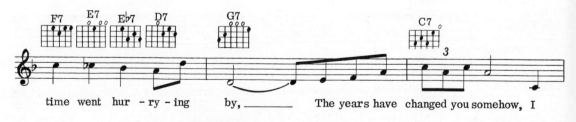

time went hur - ry - ing by,_____ The years have changed you somehow, I

78
Solitude

Words by Eddie de Lange & Irving Mills
Music by Duke Ellington

79
Oh, Didn't He Ramble

Words & Music by Will Handy

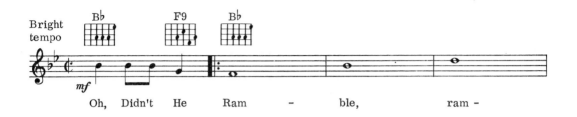

Oh, Didn't He Ram - ble, ram -

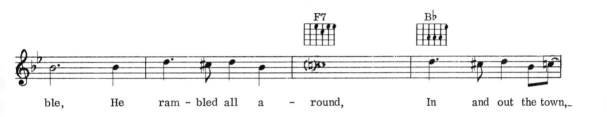

ble, He ram - bled all a - round, In and out the town,

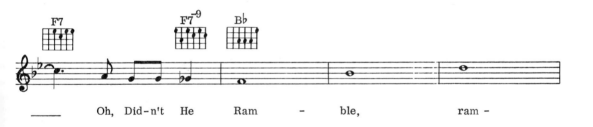

Oh, Did-n't He Ram - ble, ram -

ble, He ram - bled till the but - chers cut him down.

Oh, Did-n't He

80
South

Music by Bennie Moten & T. Hayes
Words by Ray Charles

Down be-low that old Dix-on Line,— There's a place that

real-ly is fine.— Don't you know jus' what I'm talk-in' a-bout!—

Y'wan-na find out?— Then take a trip with me, Down be-low that

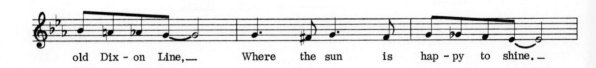

old Dix-on Line,— Where the sun is hap-py to shine.—

Where a friend-ly face is com-mon to see,— That's where I'm long-in' to be. —

81
Splanky

By Neal Hefti

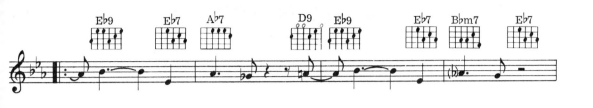

82
Stomp, Look And Listen

By Duke Ellington

83
Struttin' With Some Barbecue

Words by Don Raye
Music by Louis Armstrong

84
St. Thomas

By Sonny Rollins

85
Sunny

Words & Music by Bobby Hebb

1. Sun - ny, — yes - ter - day my life was filled with rain, —
Sun - ny, — you smiled at me and real - ly eased the pain. — Oh, the
dark days are done, — and the bright days are here, — my sun - ny one — shines
so sin - cere, — Oh Sun - ny one so true, — I love you.

2. Sun - ny, — thank you for the sun - shine — bou - quet, —
Sun - ny, — thank you for the love you've brought my way. — You
gave — to me — your — all — and all, — Now I feel — ten feet tall. — Sun - ny one so true, — I love you. —

3. Sunny, thank you for the truth you've let me see.
Sunny, thank you for the facts from A to Z.
My life was torn like wind-blown sand,
Then a rock was formed when we held hands,
Sunny one so true, I love you.

4. Sunny, thank you for that smile upon your face.
Sunny, thank you for that gleam that flows with grace.
You're my spark of nature's fire,
You're my sweet complete desire.
Sunny one so true, I love you.

86
Sweetheart Of Sigmund Freud

By Shorty Rogers

87
Sweet Sue, Just You

Words by Will J. Harris
Music by Victor Young

88
Take Five

By Paul Desmond

89
T'ain't What You Do
(It's The Way That 'Cha Do It)

Words & Music by Sy Oliver & James Young

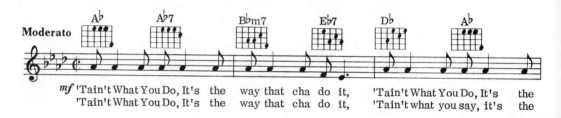

'Tain't What You Do, It's the way that cha do it, 'Tain't What You Do, It's the
'Tain't What You Do, It's the way that cha do it, 'Tain't what you say, it's the

way that cha do it. 'Tain't What You Do, it's the way that cha do it,—
way that cha say it. 'Tain't what cha say, it's the way that cha say it,—

That's what gets— re-sults.—— 'Tain't What You Do, it's the
That's what gets— re-sults.—— 'Tain't what you croon, it's the

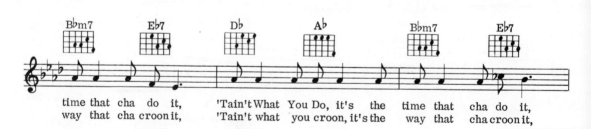

time that cha do it, 'Tain't What You Do, it's the time that cha do it,
way that cha croon it, 'Tain't what you croon, it's the way that cha croon it,

'Tain't What You Do, it's the time that cha do it,— That's what gets— re-sults.—
'Tain't what you croon, it's the way that cha croon it,— That's what gets— re-sults.—

90
Take The 'A' Train

Words & Music by Billy Strayhorn

You _____ must take the "A" train, _____ To
If _____ you miss the "A" train, _____ You'll

go to Sug - ar Hill 'way up in Har - lem. _____
find you've missed the quick - est way to Har - lem. _____

_____ Hur - ry, _____ get on now it's com - ing, _____

_____ Lis - ten _____ to those rails a - thrum - ming. _____

_____ All 'board! _____ get on the "A" train, _____

_____ Soon you will be on Sug - ar Hill in Har - lem. _____

91
Time's A-Wastin'

Words & Music by
Duke Ellington, Mercer Ellington & Don George

92
Undecided

Words by Sid Robin
Music by Charles Shavers

Bright swing

First you say you do and then you don't and then you say you will and

then you won't, you're un-de-cid-ed now, so what are you gon-na do?

Now you want to play, and then it's no, and when you say you'll stay, that's

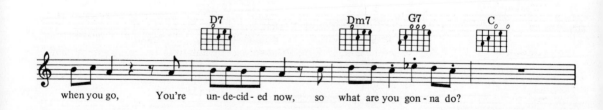

when you go, You're un-de-cid-ed now, so what are you gon-na do?

I've been sit-ting on a fence, and it does-n't make much sense, cause you

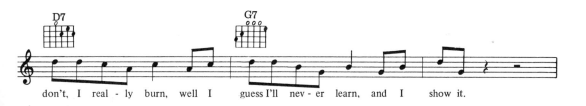

don't, I real-ly burn, well I guess I'll nev-er learn, and I show it.

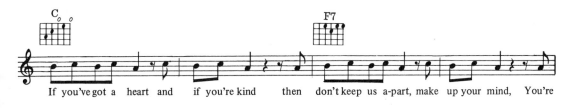

If you've got a heart and if you're kind then don't keep us a-part, make up your mind, You're

un-de-cid-ed now, so what are you gon-na do?

93
Violets For Your Furs

Words by Tom Adair
Music by Matt Dennis

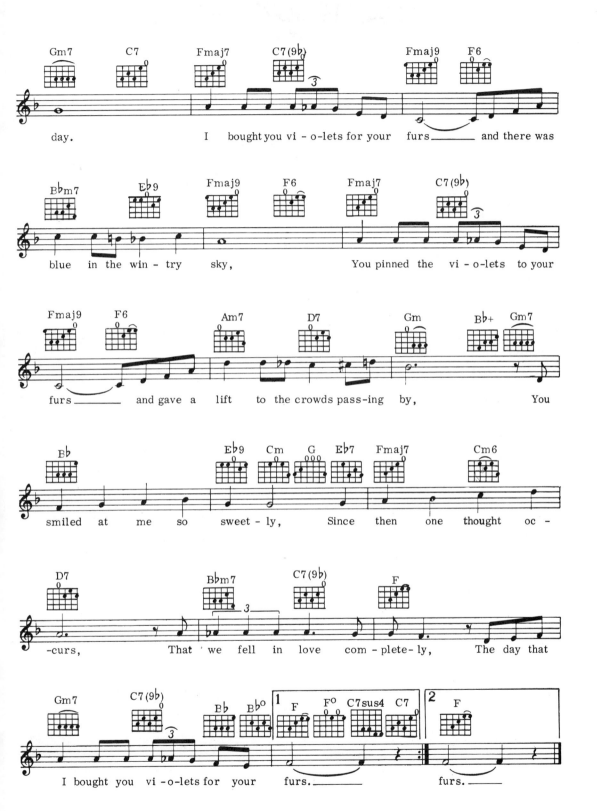

94
Walk Don't Run

By Shorty Rogers

95
Walkin' Shoes

By Gerry Mulligan

96
Wave

Words & Music by Antonio Carlos Jobim

97
Way Down Yonder In New Orleans

Words & Music by
Henry Creamer & Turner Layton

98
Ting-A-Ling

By Louis Bellson & Charles Shavers

99
When The Saints Go Marching In

Traditional

100
Woodchopper's Ball

By Joe Bishop & Woody Herman

101
Yes Indeed!
(A Jive Spiritual)

Words & Music by Sy Oliver

Jive spiritual

mf

Yes In - deed, _____ Yes In - deed, _____

_____ I've got that feel-in' _ in me, Yes In - deed. _____ You will

shout when it hits you, Yes In - deed. _____ Yes you'll
out if it's in you, Yes In - deed. _____ Makes you

shout when it hits you, Yes In - deed. When the spir - it
shout "Jack it sends you, Yes In - deed. When that jive starts

moves you, You'll shout "Hal - le - lu - jah" _____ When it
jump - in', You'll shout "Let me in there" _____ When it

hits you, _ You'll hol-la _ Yes In - deed. _____ It comes
hits you, _ You'll hol-la _ Yes In - deed. _____